GROLIER
B O O K S

Grolier Books is a division of
Grolier Enterprises, Inc.

Grolier offers a varied selection of
children's book racks and tote bags.
For details on ordering, please write:
Grolier Direct Marketing
Sherman Turnpike
Danbury, CT 06816
Att: Premium Department

My O Book

by Jane Belk Moncure
illustrated by Vera Gohman
with Linda Hohag

THE CHILD'S WORLD

Mankato, MN 56001

Little had a

He said, "I will fill my box."

Little ⬤ hopped away,

hop, hop, hop.

He found

otters

in a pond.

He put the

otters

into his box.

Little

found an octopus.

Guess where he put
the octopus?

But the otters did
not like the octopus.

The otters hopped out
of the box,

hop, hop, hop.

Little put a top on the box, so the octopus could not get out.

Then he put the otters on top
of the box.

Away he went, hop, hop, hop.

Then Little found an

ostrich.

He hopped on
the ostrich.

"Hop,"
    he said.

But the ostrich would not hop.

So Little put the ostrich on top of the box.

Now the box was heavy.

Little found an

ox.

"You are just what I need
for my box," he said.

Away they went,
hop,
hop,

all the way home.

Little took his things
out of his box.

octopus

ox

24

ostrich

otters

What funny things he had!

More words with Little .

S	M	T	W	T	F	S
	1	2	3	4	5	6
7	8	9	10	11	12	13
14	15	16	17	18	19	20
21	22	23	24	25	26	27
28	29	30	31			

October

olives

ocelot

operator

omnibus

Little has another sound in some words.

He says his name.

Listen for Little 's name.

overalls

okra

oatmeal

opal

ocean